Ommie
and The Magical Garden

Written and illustrated by Sirkka Fisk

www.ommie.co.uk

My eyes are closed. Am I dreaming?

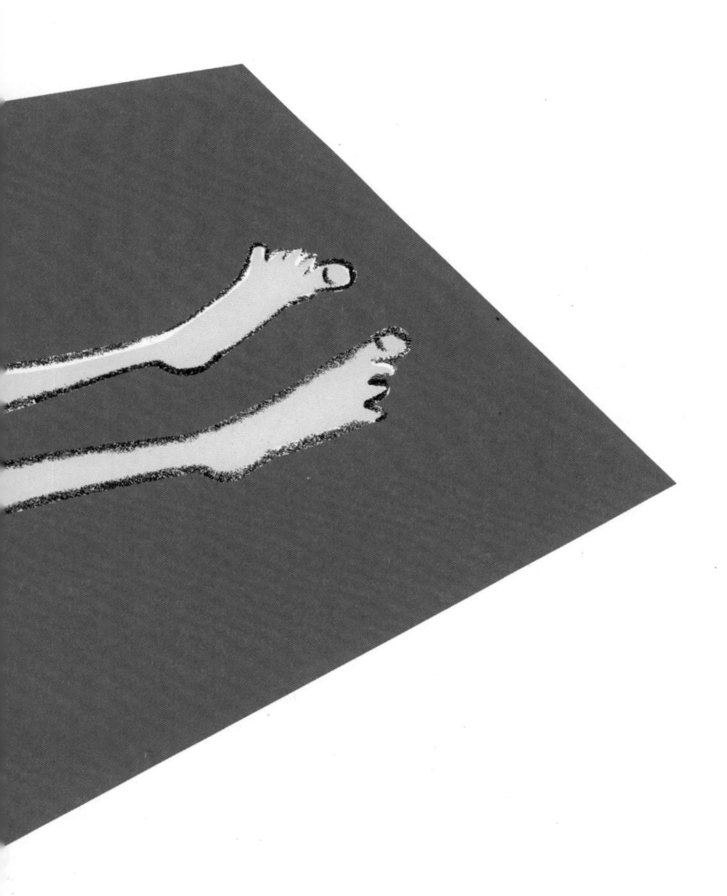

I am in a garden with trees so tall.
I see bright coloured flowers over a wall.

I take a deeeeep breath.

I stretch up my arms.
How tall can I be?
Wake up body!
There is so much to see.

I take deep breaths, **1**, and **2**, and **3**,
Is there anyone here, other than me?

"Hello. Is this your magical garden?"

“Not mine to own, I am passing through too.

I am a cow and stand on all fours,
I give lots of milk, but I always have more.”

"Hello. Is this your magical garden?"

"Not mine to own,
I am passing
through too.

I am a pussy cat,
shiny and black,
I curl my tail and
arch my back."

"Hello. Is this your magical garden?"

"Not mine to own, I am passing through too.
I am a cobra, slithery and shy. I get frightened, then rise up high."

"Hello. Is this your magical garden?"

"Not mine to own, I am passing through too.

I am a dog and love to play; then lie down for a nap and have a good snore.

And after a doze I stretch and stretch, from my waggling tail to furry paw."

"Hello. Is this your magical garden?"

"Not mine to own, I am passing through too.
I am a grey dormouse, as small as can be,
and I rest quietly, so no one can see."

“Hello. Is this your magical garden?”

rrrooooaaaaaaaaaar!!!!!!!

"Not mine to own, I am passing through too. I am a lion with mighty great paws, I have a loud voice and love to roar."

"Hello. Is this your magical garden?"

"Not mine to own, I am passing through too. I am a butterfly with wings stretched wide, searching for flowers as I flutter and dive!"

"Hello. Is this your magical garden?"

"Not mine to own, I am passing through too. I am a swan, graceful and strong.

I pull back my wings, as I swim along."

"Hello. Is this your magical garden?"

"Not mine to own, I am passing through too. I am a hedgehog.
I curl up in a ball, spiky and round.
I roll in the leaves and blend in with the ground."

"Hello. Is this your magical garden?"

"Not mine to own, I am passing through too.

I am a crocodile, green and long.

I slide through the river, slowly gliding along."

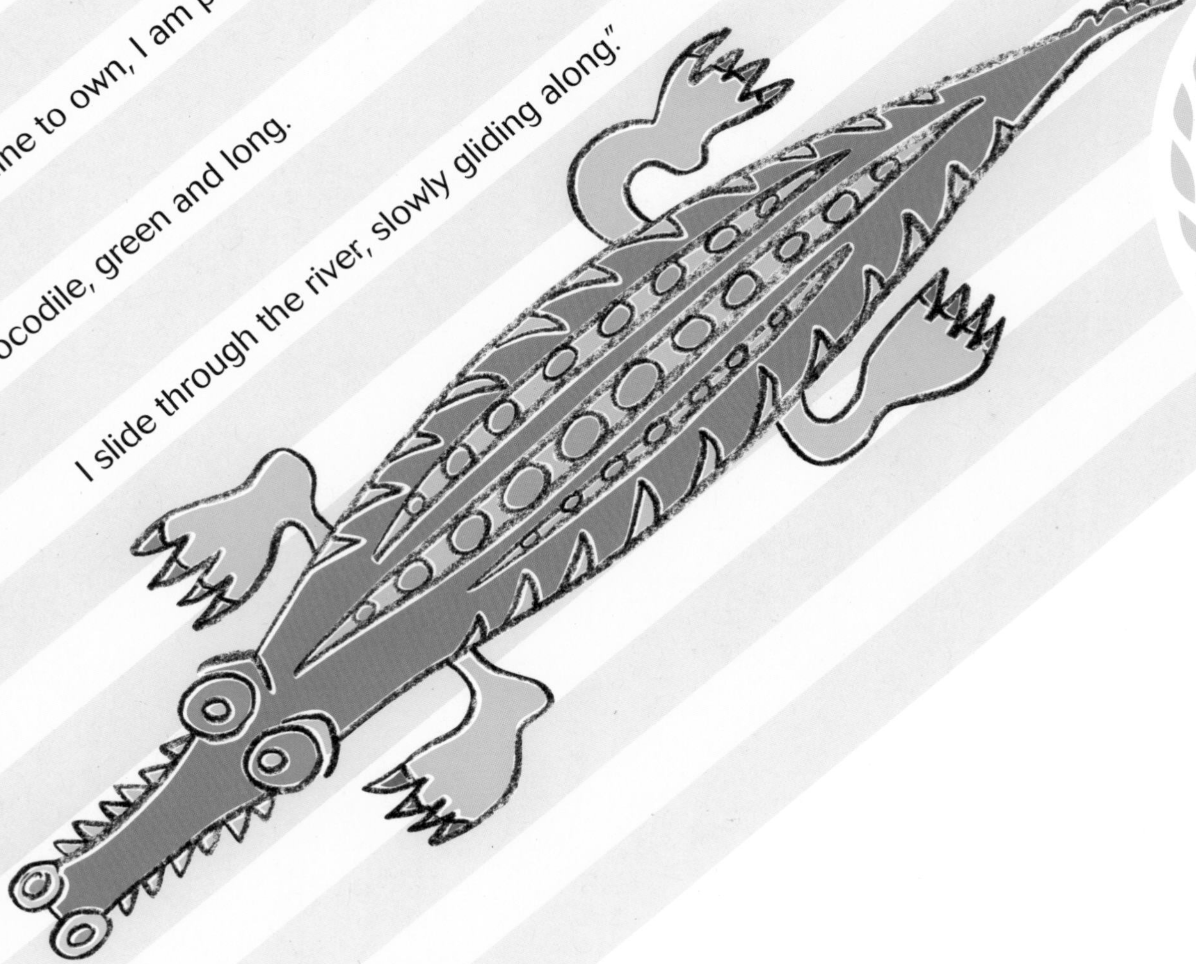

I stand still.

The animals are gone.

The trees stand silent and tall not moving at all.

I stand on my toes, reaching up
As I look around, I see my friends are
This magical garden is not mine or
This magical garden is for
smiling

bove me, a rainbow shines bright in the sky.
nd as one big family, we all belong here!
is magical garden is ours to share.
nd we pass through it together,
e sun.

Now I lie very still and I close my eyes.

I am feeling happy and peaceful inside.